Scripture Scri

PRIMARY
VOLUME II

My Whole Heart

CONCEIVED & WRITTEN BY
MARY ELLEN TEDROW-WYNN

COVER, LAYOUT DESIGN, & TYPESETTING BY
ALLISON ARMERDING

Dedication

This book is dedicated to my very special sister Kitty, whom I love with "My Whole Heart." You have been there for me my whole life, helping me, cheering me on, encouraging me, forgiving me, loving me. When I need it, you are my sister, or my friend, or my mom, or my counselor. You listen without judgement. You help without worrying the cost.

Kitty, I love you to the moon and back.
You are "the click to answer my clack"!

God gave me something very special when He made you my sister. I love you . . . with my whole heart!

I will praise You, O Lord, with my whole heart;
I will tell of all Your marvelous works.
Psalm 9:1 NKJV

Copyright

Scripture Scribes: My Whole Heart
Laurelwood Books © 2016
ISBN: 978-1-941383-28-5

We have checked for errors in this text. However, should you notice any mistakes, we would love to hear from you.
Please contact us at *marylnw7@gmail.com*

Schools and/or co-ops, please contact us for group discounts.

Find this and other great books on our website:
www.laurelwoodbooks.com
You may also reach us at:
Laurelwood Books
1639 Ebenezer Road
Bluemont, VA 20135

Scripture Scribes

Scripture Scribes is copy work for students to write and fall in love with the Scriptures.

Scripture Scribes: My Whole Heart features:

- 30 week-long lessons using several English translations of the Bible
- Reading Scripture
- Tracing Scripture
- Copying Scripture

. . . reminding me to love God with "my whole heart."

Alphabet Practice! Trace the letters.

A a B b C c D d E e F f G g

Alphabet Practice! Trace the letters.

Alphabet Practice! Trace the letters.

O

o

P

p

Q

q

R

r

S

s

T

t

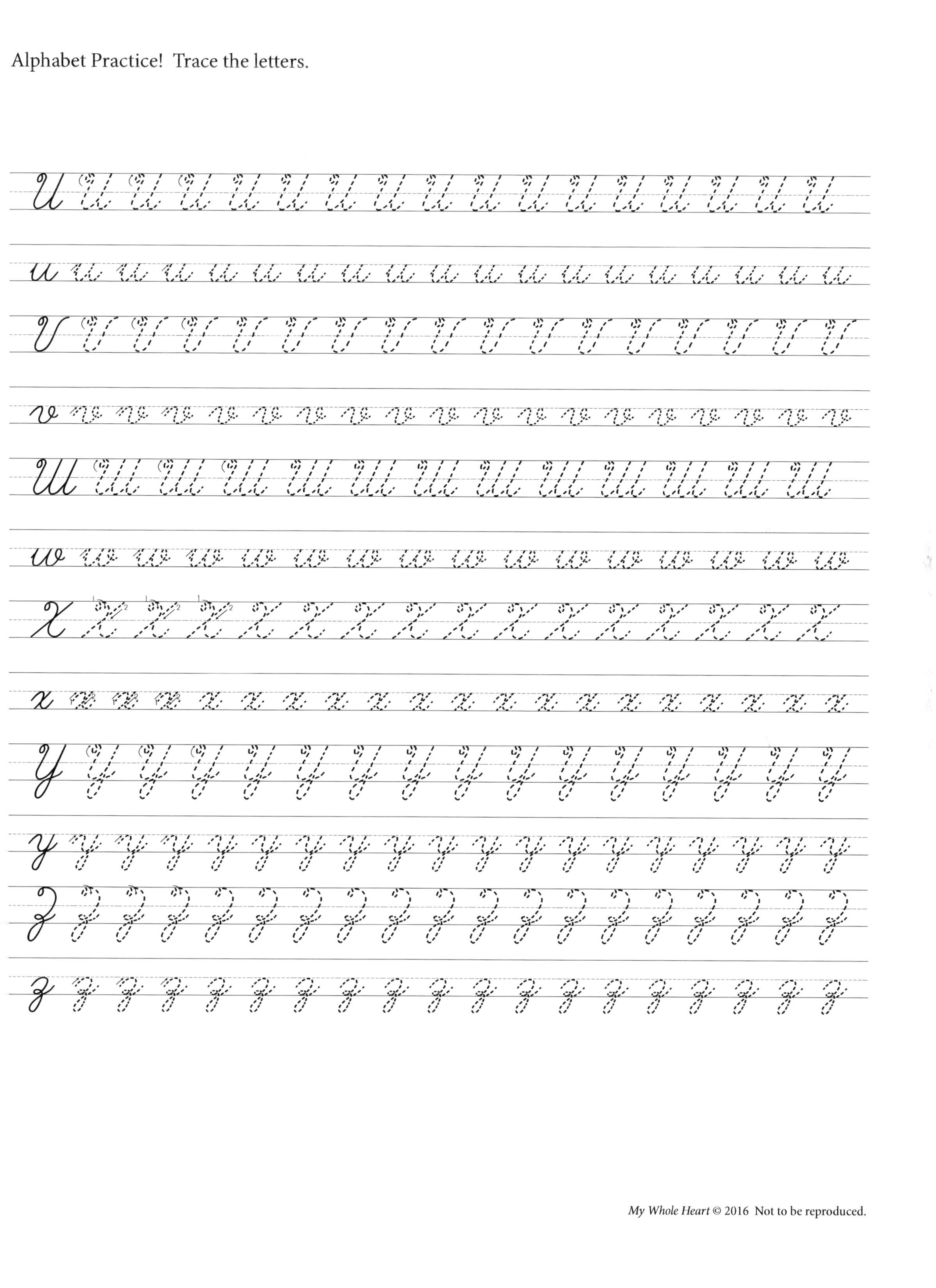

Alphabet Practice! Trace the letters.

U

u

V

v

W

w

X

x

Y

y

Z

z

Lesson 1: Day 1

"... for each tree is known by its own fruit...
The good person out of the good treasure of his heart produces good, and the evil person out of his evil treasure produces evil, for out of the abundance of the heart his mouth speaks."
Luke 6:44a-45 ESV

Trace and copy the verse below.

"... for each tree is known

by its own fruit..."

"... for each tree is known

by its own fruit..."

Lesson 1: Day 2

"... for each tree is known by its own fruit ...
The good person out of the good treasure of his heart produces good, and the evil person out of his evil treasure produces evil, for out of the abundance of the heart his mouth speaks."
Luke 6:44a-45 ESV

Trace and copy the verse below.

"The good person
out of the good treasure
of his heart produces good..."

"The good person
out of the good treasure
of his heart produces good..."

Lesson 1: Day 3

"... for each tree is known by its own fruit . . .
The good person out of the good treasure of his heart produces good, **and the evil person out of his evil treasure produces evil,** for out of the abundance of the heart his mouth speaks."
Luke 6:44a-45 ESV

Trace and copy the verse below.

". . . and the evil person
out of his evil treasure
produces evil."

". . . and the evil person
out of his evil treasure
produces evil."

Lesson 1: Day 4

"... for each tree is known by its own fruit . . .
The good person out of the good treasure of his heart produces good, and the evil person out of his evil treasure produces evil, **for out of the abundance of the heart his mouth speaks.**"
Luke 6:44a-45 ESV

Trace the verse below.

". . . for out of the abundance
of the heart
his mouth speaks."

". . . for out of the abundance
of the heart
his mouth speaks."

Lesson 2: Day 1

But the LORD said to Samuel, "Do not look at his appearance or at his physical stature, because I have refused him. For the LORD does not see as man sees; for man looks at the outward appearance, but the LORD looks at the heart."
1 Samuel 16:7 NKJV

Trace and copy the verse below.

But the LORD said to Samuel,

"Do not look

at his appearance . . ."

But the LORD said to Samuel,

"Do not look

at his appearance . . ."

Lesson 2: Day 2

But the LORD said to Samuel, "Do not look at his appearance **or at his physical stature, because I have refused him.** For the LORD does not see as man sees; for man looks at the outward appearance, but the LORD looks at the heart."
1 Samuel 16:7 NKJV

Trace and copy the verse below.

". . . or at his physical stature,

because I have refused him."

". . . or at his physical stature,

because I have refused him."

". . . or at his physical stature,

because I have refused him."

Lesson 2: Day 3

> But the LORD said to Samuel, "Do not look at his appearance or at his physical stature, because I have refused him. **For the LORD does not see as man sees;** for man looks at the outward appearance, but the LORD looks at the heart."
> 1 Samuel 16:7 NKJV

Trace and copy the verse below.

"For the LORD does not see

as man sees . . ."

"For the LORD does not see

as man sees . . ."

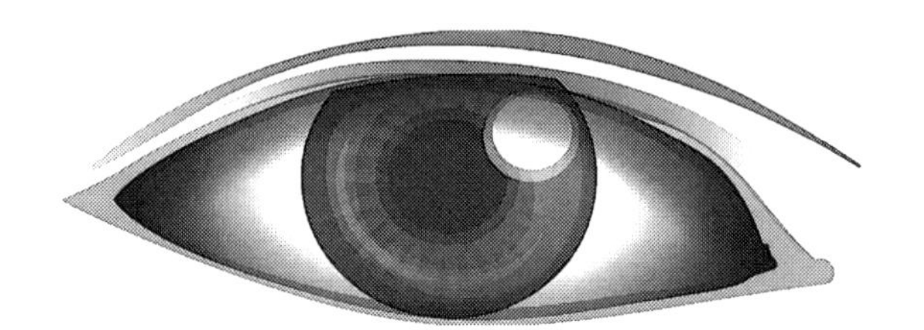
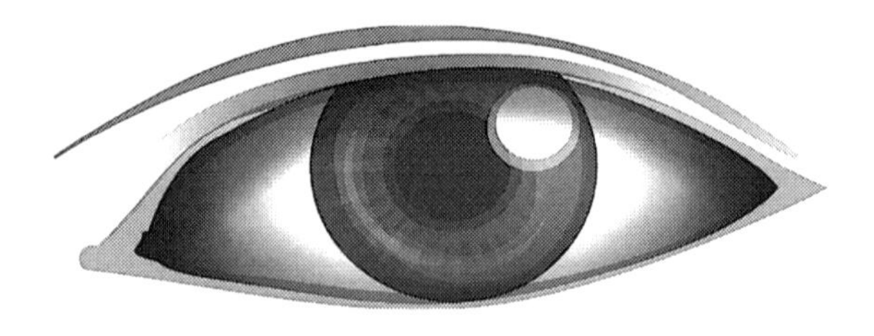

Lesson 2: 1 Samuel 16:7

But the LORD said to Samuel, "Do not look at his appearance or at his physical stature, because I have refused him. For the LORD does not see as man sees; **for man looks at the outward appearance, but the LORD looks at the heart."**
1 Samuel 16:7 NKJV

Trace and copy the verse below.

". . . for man looks at the
outward appearance, but the LORD
looks at the heart."

". . . for man looks at the
outward appearance, but the LORD
looks at the heart."

Lesson 3: Day 1

Create in me a pure heart, O God, and renew a steadfast spirit within me.
My sacrifice, O God, is a broken spirit; a broken and contrite heart you, God, will not despise.
Psalm 51:10, 17 NIV

Trace and copy the verse below.

Create in me a pure heart,

O God . . .

Create in me a pure heart,

O God . . .

Create in me a pure heart,

O God . . .

Lesson 3: Day 2

Create in me a pure heart, O God, **and renew a steadfast spirit within me.**
My sacrifice, O God, is a broken spirit; a broken and contrite heart you, God, will not despise.
Psalm 51:10, 17 NIV

Trace and copy the verse below.

. . . and renew a steadfast

spirit within me.

. . . and renew a steadfast

spirit within me.

. . . and renew a steadfast

spirit within me.

Lesson 3: Day 3

Create in me a pure heart, O God, and renew a steadfast spirit within me.
My sacrifice, O God, is a broken spirit; a broken and contrite heart you, God, will not despise.
Psalm 51:10, 17 NIV

Trace and copy the verse below.

My sacrifice, O God,

is a broken spirit . . .

My sacrifice, O God,

is a broken spirit . . .

My sacrifice, O God,

is a broken spirit . . .

Lesson 3: Day 4

Create in me a pure heart, O God, and renew a steadfast spirit within me.
My sacrifice, O God, is a broken spirit; **a broken and contrite heart you, God, will not despise.**
Psalm 51:10, 17 NIV

Trace and copy the verse below.

. . . a broken and contrite heart

you, God, will not despise.

. . . a broken and contrite heart

you, God, will not despise.

. . . a broken and contrite heart

you, God, will not despise.

Lesson 4: Day 1

And I will give you a new heart, and a new spirit I will put within you.
And I will remove the heart of stone from your flesh and give you a heart of flesh.
Ezekiel 36:26 ESV

Trace and copy the verse below.

And I will give you

a new heart . . .

And I will give you

a new heart . . .

And I will give you

a new heart . . .

Lesson 4: Day 2

And I will give you a new heart, **and a new spirit I will put within you.**
And I will remove the heart of stone from your flesh and give you a heart of flesh.
Ezekiel 36:26 ESV

Trace and copy the verse below.

. . . and a new spirit

I will put within you.

. . . and a new spirit

I will put within you.

. . . and a new spirit

I will put within you.

Lesson 4: Day 3

And I will give you a new heart, and a new spirit I will put within you.
And I will remove the heart of stone from your flesh and give you a heart of flesh.
Ezekiel 36:26 ESV

Trace and copy the verse below.

And I will remove the heart

of stone from your flesh . . .

And I will remove the heart

of stone from your flesh . . .

And I will remove the heart

of stone from your flesh . . .

Lesson 4: Day 4

And I will give you a new heart, and a new spirit I will put within you.
And I will remove the heart of stone from your flesh **and give you a heart of flesh.**
Ezekiel 36:26 ESV

Trace and copy the verse below.

. . . and give you

a heart of flesh.

. . . and give you

a heart of flesh.

. . . and give you

a heart of flesh.

Lesson 5: Day 1

Keep your heart with all diligence,
For out of it spring the issues of life.
Put away from you a deceitful mouth,
And put perverse lips far from you.
Proverbs 4:23-24 NKJV

Trace and copy the verse below.

Keep your heart

with all diligence . . .

Keep your heart

with all diligence . . .

Lesson 5: Day 2

Keep your heart with all diligence,
For out of it spring the issues of life.
Put away from you a deceitful mouth,
And put perverse lips far from you.
Proverbs 4:23-24 NKJV

Trace and copy the verse below.

For out of it spring

the issues of life.

For out of it spring

the issues of life.

For out of it spring

the issues of life.

Lesson 5: Day 3

Keep your heart with all diligence,
For out of it spring the issues of life.
Put away from you a deceitful mouth,
And put perverse lips far from you.
Proverbs 4:23-24 NKJV

Trace and copy the verse below.

Put away from you

a deceitful mouth . . .

Put away from you

a deceitful mouth . . .

Put away from you

a deceitful mouth . . .

Lesson 5: Day 4

Keep your heart with all diligence,
For out of it spring the issues of life.
Put away from you a deceitful mouth,
And put perverse lips far from you.
Proverbs 4:23-24 NKJV

Trace and copy the verse below.

And put perverse lips

far from you.

And put perverse lips

far from you.

And put perverse lips

far from you.

Lesson 6: Day 1

As for that in the good soil, they are those who, hearing the word, hold it fast in an honest and good heart, and bear fruit with patience.
Luke 8:15 ESV

Trace and copy the verse below.

As for that

in the good soil . . .

As for that

in the good soil . . .

As for that

in the good soil . . .

Lesson 6: Day 2

As for that in the good soil, **they are those who, hearing the word,** hold it fast in an honest and good heart, and bear fruit with patience.
Luke 8:15 ESV

Trace and copy the verse below.

. . . they are those who,

hearing the word . . .

. . . they are those who,

hearing the word . . .

. . . they are those who,

hearing the word . . .

Lesson 6: Day 3

As for that in the good soil, they are those who, hearing the word,
hold it fast in an honest and good heart, and bear fruit with patience.
Luke 8:15 ESV

Trace and copy the verse below.

. . . hold it fast in an

honest and good heart . . .

. . . hold it fast in an

honest and good heart . . .

. . . hold it fast in an

honest and good heart . . .

Lesson 6: Day 4

As for that in the good soil, they are those who, hearing the word,
hold it fast in an honest and good heart, **and bear fruit with patience.**
Luke 8:15 ESV

Trace and copy the verse below.

. . . and bear fruit

with patience.

. . . and bear fruit

with patience.

Lesson 7: Day 1

Do not be carried about with various and strange doctrines.
For it is good that the heart be established by grace,
not with foods which have not profited those who have been occupied with them.
Hebrews 13:9 NKJV

Trace and copy the verse below.

Do not be carried about

with various and strange doctrines.

Do not be carried about

with various and strange doctrines.

Do not be carried about

with various and strange doctrines.

Lesson 7: Day 2

Do not be carried about with various and strange doctrines.
For it is good that the heart be established by grace,
not with foods which have not profited those who have been occupied with them.
Hebrews 13:9 NKJV

Trace and copy the verse below.

For it is good that the heart

be established by grace . . .

For it is good that the heart

be established by grace . . .

For it is good that the heart

be established by grace . . .

Lesson 7: Day 3

Do not be carried about with various and strange doctrines.
For it is good that the heart be established by grace,
not with foods which have not profited those who have been occupied with them.
Hebrews 13:9 NKJV

Trace and copy the verse below.

. . . not with foods

which have not profited those . . .

. . . not with foods

which have not profited those . . .

. . . not with foods

which have not profited those . . .

Lesson 7: Day 4

Do not be carried about with various and strange doctrines.
For it is good that the heart be established by grace,
not with foods which have not profited those **who have been occupied with them.**
Hebrews 13:9 NKJV

Trace and copy the verse below.

. . . who have been
occupied with them.

. . . who have been
occupied with them.

. . . who have been
occupied with them.

Lesson 8: Day 1

The LORD saw that the wickedness of man was great in the earth,
and that every intention of the thoughts of his heart was only evil continually.
Genesis 6:5 ESV

Trace and copy the verse below.

The Lord saw

that the wickedness . . .

The Lord saw

that the wickedness . . .

The Lord saw

that the wickedness . . .

Lesson 8: Day 2

The LORD saw that the wickedness **of man was great in the earth,**
and that every intention of the thoughts of his heart was only evil continually.
Genesis 6:5 ESV

Trace and copy the verse below.

. . . of man was great

in the earth.

. . . of man was great

in the earth.

Lesson 8: Day 3

The LORD saw that the wickedness of man was great in the earth,
and that every intention of the thoughts of his heart was only evil continually.
Genesis 6:5 ESV

Trace and copy the verse below.

. . . and that every intention

of the thoughts . . .

. . . and that every intention

of the thoughts . . .

. . . and that every intention

of the thoughts . . .

Lesson 8: Day 4

The LORD saw that the wickedness of man was great in the earth,
and that every intention of the thoughts **of his heart was only evil continually.**
Genesis 6:5 ESV

Trace and copy the verse below.

. . . of his heart was

only evil continually.

. . . of his heart was

only evil continually.

. . . of his heart was

only evil continually.

Lesson 9: Day 1

Love the Lord your God with all your heart and with all your soul
and with all your mind and with all your strength.
Mark 12:30 NIV

Trace and copy the verse below.

Love the Lord your God

with all your heart . . .

Love the Lord your God

with all your heart . . .

Love the Lord your God

with all your heart . . .

Lesson 9: Day 2

Love the Lord your God with all your heart **and with all your soul**
and with all your mind and with all your strength.
Mark 12:30 NIV

Trace and copy the verse below.

. . . and with all

your soul . . .

. . . and with all

your soul . . .

. . . and with all

your soul . . .

Lessson 9: Day 3

Love the Lord your God with all your heart and with all your soul
and with all your mind and with all your strength.
Mark 12:30 NIV

Trace and copy the verse below.

. . . and with all

your mind . . .

. . . and with all

your mind . . .

Lesson 9: Day 4

Love the Lord your God with all your heart and with all your soul
and with all your mind **and with all your strength.**
Mark 12:30 NIV

Trace and copy the verse below.

. . . and with all

your strength.

. . . and with all

your strength.

. . . and with all

your strength.

Lesson 10: Day 1

With my whole heart I have sought You;
Oh, let me not wander from Your commandments!
Your word I have hidden in my heart,
That I might not sin against You.
Psalm 119:10-11 NKJV

Trace and copy the verse below.

With my whole heart

I have sought You;

With my whole heart

I have sought You;

With my whole heart

I have sought You;

Lesson 10: Day 2

With my whole heart I have sought You;
Oh, let me not wander from Your commandments!
Your word I have hidden in my heart,
That I might not sin against You.
Psalm 119:10-11 NKJV

Trace and copy the verse below.

Oh, let me not wander

from Your commandments!

Oh, let me not wander

from Your commandments!

Oh, let me not wander

from Your commandments!

Lesson 10: Day 3

With my whole heart I have sought You;
Oh, let me not wander from Your commandments!
Your word I have hidden in my heart,
That I might not sin against You.
Psalm 119:10-11 NKJV

Trace and copy the verse below.

Your word I have

hidden in my heart,

Your word I have

hidden in my heart,

Lesson 10: Day 4

With my whole heart I have sought You;
Oh, let me not wander from Your commandments!
Your word I have hidden in my heart,
That I might not sin against You.
Psalm 119:10-11 NKJV

Trace and copy the verse below.

That I might not

sin against You.

That I might not

sin against You.

That I might not

sin against You.

Bible History

The word "Bible" comes from the Greek work *biblia*, which means "books." The Bible is a collection of many books. It took many many years--about 1100--to gather them all together in what we now call the Bible.

When the books were written, they did not have computers, or typewriters, or even paper as we do today. They had *papyrus*, a paper-like material made out of reeds, or dried animal skin called *vellum*. Can you imagine writing on such things? We are so accustomed to having lots of paper, it is hard for us to think about writing a book report or a whole book using only these materials.

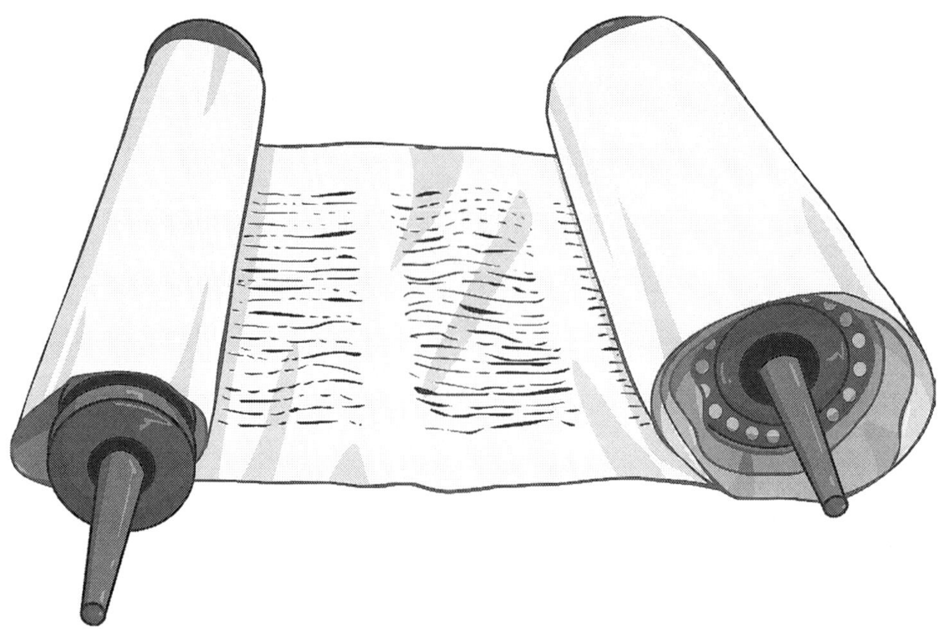

Bible History

Oh, and they didn't have pens or pencils like we do. They had quills pens which were made from the feathers of birds. It probably sounds like a lot of fun but if you had to do it all the time for all your writing, you might get tired of it.

Try finding a large feather, cutting the end off of the shaft, dipping it in ink and try writing like the scribes of old!

Lesson 11: Day 1

Do not let your heart envy sinners,
but rather be zealous in fearing the LORD all the time. . .
Listen, my child, and be wise,
and guide your heart on the right way.
Proverbs 23:17, 19 NET

Trace and copy the verse below.

Do not let your

heart envy sinners . . .

Do not let your

heart envy sinners . . .

Do not let your

heart envy sinners . . .

Lesson 11: Day 2

Do not let your heart envy sinners,
but rather be zealous in fearing the LORD all the time...
Listen, my child, and be wise,
and guide your heart on the right way.
Proverbs 23:17, 19 NET

Trace and copy the verse below.

. . . but rather be zealous

in fearing the Lord all the time . . .

. . . but rather be zealous

in fearing the Lord all the time . . .

. . . but rather be zealous

in fearing the Lord all the time . . .

Lesson 11: Day 3

Do not let your heart envy sinners,
but rather be zealous in fearing the LORD all the time. . .
Listen, my child, and be wise,
and guide your heart on the right way.
Proverbs 23:17, 19 NET

Trace and copy the verse below.

Listen, my child,

and be wise . . .

Listen, my child,

and be wise . . .

Listen, my child,

and be wise . . .

Lesson 11: Day 4

Do not let your heart envy sinners,
but rather be zealous in fearing the LORD all the time. . .
Listen, my child, and be wise,
and guide your heart on the right way.
Proverbs 23:17, 19 NET

Trace and copy the verse below.

. . . and guide your heart

on the right way.

. . . and guide your heart

on the right way.

Lessson 12: Day 1

And the LORD smelled a soothing aroma. Then the LORD said in His heart,
"I will never again curse the ground for man's sake, although the imagination of man's heart is evil from his youth; nor will I again destroy every living thing as I have done.
Genesis 8:21 NKJV

Trace and copy the verse below.

And the LORD smelled a soothing aroma.

Then the LORD said in His heart . . .

And the LORD smelled a soothing aroma.

Then the LORD said in His heart . . .

Lesson 12: Day 2

And the LORD smelled a soothing aroma. Then the LORD said in His heart, **"I will never again curse the ground for man's sake,** although the imagination of man's heart is evil from his youth; nor will I again destroy every living thing as I have done.
Genesis 8:21 NKJV

Trace and copy the verse below.

"I will never again curse

the ground for man's sake . . ."

"I will never again curse

the ground for man's sake . . ."

"I will never again curse

the ground for man's sake . . ."

Lessen 12: Day 3

And the LORD smelled a soothing aroma. Then the LORD said in His heart,
"I will never again curse the ground for man's sake, **although the imagination of man's heart is evil from his youth;** nor will I again destroy every living thing as I have done.
Genesis 8:21 NKJV

Trace and copy the verse below.

". . . although the imagination of

man's heart is evil from his youth . . ."

". . . although the imagination of

man's heart is evil from his youth . . ."

". . . although the imagination of

man's heart is evil from his youth . . ."

Lesson 12: Day 4

And the LORD smelled a soothing aroma. Then the LORD said in His heart, "I will never again curse the ground for man's sake, although the imagination of man's heart is evil from his youth; **nor will I again destroy every living thing as I have done.**

Genesis 8:21 NKJV

Trace and copy the verse below.

". . . nor will I again destroy

every living thing as I have done."

". . . nor will I again destroy

every living thing as I have done."

". . . nor will I again destroy

every living thing as I have done."

Lesson 13: Day 1

Then you will call upon me and come and pray to me, and I will hear you.
You will seek me and find me, when you seek me with all your heart.
Jeremiah 29:12-13 ESV

Trace and copy the verse below.

Then you will call

upon me and come . . .

Then you will call

upon me and come . . .

Then you will call

upon me and come . . .

Lesson 13: Day 2

Then you will call upon me and come **and pray to me, and I will hear you.**
You will seek me and find me, when you seek me with all your heart.
Jeremiah 29:12-13 ESV

Trace and copy the verse below.

. . . and pray to me,

and I will hear you.

. . . and pray to me,

and I will hear you.

Lessson 13: Day 3

Then you will call upon me and come and pray to me, and I will hear you.
You will seek me and find me, when you seek me with all your heart.
Jeremiah 29:12-13 ESV

Trace and copy the verse below.

You will seek me

and find me . . .

You will seek me

and find me . . .

You will seek me

and find me . . .

Lesson 13: Day 4

Then you will call upon me and come and pray to me, and I will hear you.
You will seek me and find me, **when you seek me with all your heart.**
Jeremiah 29:12-13 ESV

Trace and copy the verse below.

. . . when you seek me

with all your heart.

. . . when you seek me

with all your heart.

. . . when you seek me

with all your heart.

Lesson 14: Day 1

Blessed are those who keep his statutes and seek him with all their heart–
they do no wrong but follow his ways . . .
Though the arrogant have smeared me with lies, I keep your precepts with all my heart.
Their hearts are callous and unfeeling, but I delight in your law.
Psalm 119:2-3, 69-70 NIV

Trace and copy the verse below.

Blessed are those who keep his statutes

and seek him with all their heart—

Blessed are those who keep his statutes

and seek him with all their heart—

Blessed are those who keep his statutes

and seek him with all their heart—

Lesson 14: Day 2

Blessed are those who keep his statutes and seek him with all their heart–
they do no wrong but follow his ways . . .
Though the arrogant have smeared me with lies, I keep your precepts with all my heart.
Their hearts are callous and unfeeling, but I delight in your law.
Psalm 119:2-3, 69-70 NIV

Trace and copy the verse below.

. . . they do no wrong

but follow his ways . . .

. . . they do no wrong

but follow his ways . . .

. . . they do no wrong

but follow his ways . . .

Lesson 14: Day 3

Blessed are those who keep his statutes and seek him with all their heart–
they do no wrong but follow his ways . . .
Though the arrogant have smeared me with lies, I keep your precepts with all my heart.
Their hearts are callous and unfeeling, but I delight in your law.
Psalm 119:2-3, 69-70 NIV

Trace and copy the verse below.

Though the arrogant have

smeared me with lies,

I keep your precepts with all my heart.

Though the arrogant have

smeared me with lies,

I keep your precepts with all my heart.

Lesson 14 : Day 4

Blessed are those who keep his statutes and seek him with all their heart–
they do no wrong but follow his ways . . .
Though the arrogant have smeared me with lies, I keep your precepts with all my heart.
Their hearts are callous and unfeeling, but I delight in your law.
Psalm 119:2-3, 69-70 NIV

Trace and copy the verse below.

Their hearts are callous and unfeeling,

but I delight in your law.

Their hearts are callous and unfeeling,

but I delight in your law.

Lesson 15: Day 1

For the word of God is living and active, sharper than any two-edged sword,
piercing to the division of soul and of spirit, of joints and of marrow,
and discerning the thoughts and intentions of the heart.
Hebrews 4:12 ESV

Trace and copy the verse below.

For the word of God

is living and active . . .

For the word of God

is living and active . . .

For the word of God

is living and active . . .

Lesson 15 : Day 2

For the word of God is living and active, **sharper than any two-edged sword,**
piercing to the division of soul and of spirit, of joints and of marrow,
and discerning the thoughts and intentions of the heart.
Hebrews 4:12 ESV

Trace and copy the verse below.

. . . sharper than

any two-edged sword . . .

. . . sharper than

any two-edged sword . . .

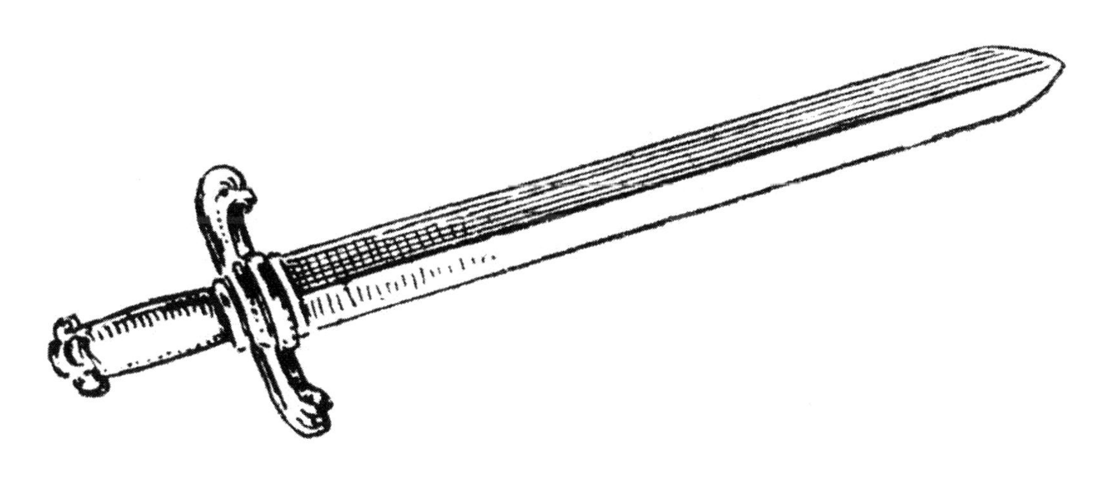

Lesson 15: Day 3

For the word of God is living and active, sharper than any two-edged sword,
piercing to the division of soul and of spirit, of joints and of marrow,
and discerning the thoughts and intentions of the heart.
Hebrews 4:12 ESV

Trace and copy the verse below.

. . . piercing to the division

of soul and of spirit,

of joints and of marrow . . .

. . . piercing to the division

of soul and of spirit,

of joints and of marrow . . .

Lesson 15: Day 4

For the word of God is living and active, sharper than any two-edged sword,
piercing to the division of soul and of spirit, of joints and of marrow,
and discerning the thoughts and intentions of the heart.
Hebrews 4:12 ESV

Trace and copy the verse below.

. . . and discerning the thoughts

and intentions of the heart.

. . . and discerning the thoughts

and intentions of the heart.

. . . and discerning the thoughts

and intentions of the heart.

Lesson 16: Day 1

Teach me Your way, O LORD; I will walk in Your truth;
Unite my heart to fear Your name.
I will praise You, O Lord my God, with all my heart,
And I will glorify Your name forevermore.
Psalm 86:11-12 NKJV

Trace and copy the verse below.

Teach me Your way, O Lord;

I will walk in Your truth;

Teach me Your way, O Lord;

I will walk in Your truth;

Teach me Your way, O Lord;

I will walk in Your truth;

Lesson 16: Day 2

Teach me Your way, O LORD; I will walk in Your truth;
Unite my heart to fear Your name.
I will praise You, O Lord my God, with all my heart,
And I will glorify Your name forevermore.
Psalm 86:11-12 NKJV

Trace and copy the verse below.

Unite my heart

to fear Your name.

Unite my heart

to fear Your name.

Unite my heart

to fear Your name.

Lesson 16: Day 3

Teach me Your way, O LORD; I will walk in Your truth;
Unite my heart to fear Your name.
I will praise You, O Lord my God, with all my heart,
And I will glorify Your name forevermore.
Psalm 86:11-12 NKJV

Trace and copy the verse below.

I will praise You, O Lord my God,

with all my heart . . .

I will praise You, O Lord my God,

with all my heart . . .

I will praise You, O Lord my God,

with all my heart . . .

Lessson 16: Day 4

Teach me Your way, O LORD; I will walk in Your truth;
Unite my heart to fear Your name.
I will praise You, O Lord my God, with all my heart,
And I will glorify Your name forevermore.
Psalm 86:11-12 NKJV

Trace and copy the verse below.

And I will glorify

Your name forevermore.

And I will glorify

Your name forevermore.

And I will glorify

Your name forevermore.

Lesson 17: Day 1

I will give them a heart to know that I am the LORD, and they shall be my people
and I will be their God, for they shall return to me with their whole heart.
Jeremiah 24:7 ESV

Trace and copy the verse below.

I will give them a heart

to know that I am the Lord . . .

I will give them a heart

to know that I am the Lord . . .

I will give them a heart

to know that I am the Lord . . .

Lesson 17: Day 2

I will give them a heart to know that I am the LORD, **and they shall be my people** and I will be their God, for they shall return to me with their whole heart.
Jeremiah 24:7 ESV

Trace and copy the verse below.

. . . and they shall

be my people . . .

. . . and they shall

be my people . . .

. . . and they shall

be my people . . .

Lesson 17: Day 3

I will give them a heart to know that I am the LORD, and they shall be my people
and I will be their God, for they shall return to me with their whole heart.
Jeremiah 24:7 ESV

Trace and copy the verse below.

. . . and I will be

their God . . .

. . . and I will be

their God . . .

. . . and I will be

their God . . .

Lesson 17: Day 4

I will give them a heart to know that I am the LORD, and they shall be my people and I will be their God, **for they shall return to me with their whole heart.**
Jeremiah 24:7 ESV

Trace and copy the verse below.

. . . for they shall return to me

with their whole heart.

. . . for they shall return to me

with their whole heart.

. . . for they shall return to me

with their whole heart.

Lesson 18: Day 1

I will give thanks to the LORD with my whole heart;
I will recount all of your wonderful deeds.
I will be glad and exult in you;
I will sing praise to your name, O Most High.
Psalm 9:1-2 ESV

Trace and copy the verse below.

I will give thanks to the Lord

with my whole heart . . .

I will give thanks to the Lord

with my whole heart . . .

I will give thanks to the Lord

with my whole heart . . .

Lesson 18: Day 2

I will give thanks to the LORD with my whole heart;
I will recount all of your wonderful deeds.
I will be glad and exult in you;
I will sing praise to your name, O Most High.
Psalm 9:1-2 ESV

Trace and copy the verse below.

I will recount all

of your wonderful deeds.

I will recount all

of your wonderful deeds.

I will recount all

of your wonderful deeds.

Lesson 18: Day 3

I will give thanks to the LORD with my whole heart;
I will recount all of your wonderful deeds.
I will be glad and exult in you;
I will sing praise to your name, O Most High.
Psalm 9:1-2 ESV

Trace and copy the verse below.

I will be glad

and exult in you;

I will be glad

and exult in you;

I will be glad

and exult in you;

Lesson 18: Day 4

I will give thanks to the LORD with my whole heart;
I will recount all of your wonderful deeds.
I will be glad and exult in you;
I will sing praise to your name, O Most High.
Psalm 9:1-2 ESV

Trace and copy the verse below.

I will sing praise

to your name, O Most High.

I will sing praise

to your name, O Most High.

Lesson 19: Day 1

But store up for yourselves treasures in heaven, where moths and vermin do not destroy, and where thieves do not break in and steal.
For where your treasure is, there your heart will be also.
Matthew 6:20-21 NIV

Trace and copy the verse below.

"But store up for yourselves

treasures in heaven . . ."

"But store up for yourselves

treasures in heaven . . ."

"But store up for yourselves

treasures in heaven . . ."

Lesson 19: Day 2

But store up for yourselves treasures in heaven, **where moths and vermin do not destroy,**
and where thieves do not break in and steal.
For where your treasure is, there your heart will be also.
Matthew 6:20-21 NIV

Trace and copy the verse below.

". . . where moths and vermin

do not destroy . . ."

". . . where moths and vermin

do not destroy . . ."

". . . where moths and vermin

do not destroy . . ."

Lessson 19: Day 3

But store up for yourselves treasures in heaven, where moths and vermin do not destroy,
and where thieves do not break in and steal.
For where your treasure is, there your heart will be also.
Matthew 6:20-21 NIV

Trace and copy the verse below.

". . . and where thieves do not

break in and steal."

". . . and where thieves do not

break in and steal."

Lesson 19: Day 4

But store up for yourselves treasures in heaven, where moths and vermin do not destroy,
and where thieves do not break in and steal.
For where your treasure is, there your heart will be also.
Matthew 6:20-21 NIV

Trace and copy the verse below.

"For where your treasure is,

there your heart will be also."

"For where your treasure is,

there your heart will be also."

"For where your treasure is,

there your heart will be also."

Lesson 20: Day 1

The heart is deceitful above all things,
and desperately sick; who can understand it?
"I the LORD search the heart and test the mind,
to give every man according to his ways, according to the fruit of his deeds."
Jeremiah 17:9-10 ESV

Trace and copy the verse below.

The heart is deceitful

above all things . . .

The heart is deceitful

above all things . . .

The heart is deceitful

above all things . . .

Lesson 20: Day 2

The heart is deceitful above all things,
and desperately sick; who can understand it?
"I the LORD search the heart and test the mind,
to give every man according to his ways, according to the fruit of his deeds."
Jeremiah 17:9-10 ESV

Trace and copy the verse below.

. . . and desperately sick;

who can understand it?

. . . and desperately sick;

who can understand it?

. . . and desperately sick;

who can understand it?

Lesson 20: Day 3

The heart is deceitful above all things,
and desperately sick; who can understand it?
"I the LORD search the heart and test the mind,
to give every man according to his ways, according to the fruit of his deeds."
Jeremiah 17:9-10 ESV

Trace and copy the verse below.

"I the LORD search the heart
and test the mind . . ."

"I the LORD search the heart
and test the mind . . ."

"I the LORD search the heart
and test the mind . . ."

Lesson 20: Day 4

The heart is deceitful above all things,
and desperately sick; who can understand it?
"I the LORD search the heart and test the mind,
to give every man according to his ways, according to the fruit of his deeds."
Jeremiah 17:9-10 ESV

Trace and copy the verse below.

". . . to give to every man

according to his ways,

according to the fruit

of his deeds."

Translating the Scriptures

Timeline of Bible Translation

(A.D. stands for *anno Domini*--"in the year of the Lord")

180 A.D. The New Testament starts to be translated from Greek into Latin, Syriac, and Coptic.

195 A.D. The name of the first translation of the Old and New Testaments into Latin was termed Old Latin, both Testaments having been translated from the Greek. Parts of the Old Latin were found in quotes by the church father Tertullian, who lived around 160-220 A.D. in north Africa and wrote treatises on theology.

300 A.D. The Old Syriac was a translation of the New Testament from the Greek into Syriac.

300 A.D. The Coptic Versions: Coptic was spoken in four dialects in Egypt. The Bible was translated into each of these four dialects.

380 A.D. The Latin Vulgate was translated by St. Jerome. He translated into Latin the Old Testament from the He brew and the New Testament from Greek. The Latin Vulgate became the Bible of the Western Church until the Protestant Reformation in the 1500's. It continues to be the authoritative translation of the Roman Catholic Church to this day.

1380 A.D. The first English translation of the Bible was by John Wycliffe. He translated the Bible into English from the Latin Vulgate. This was a translation from a translation and not a translation from the original Hebrew and Greek. Wycliffe was forced to translate from the Latin Vulgate because he did not know Hebrew or Greek.

1440s A. D. Gutenberg invents the printing press and publishes the Gutenberg Bible in the Latin Vulgate.

1500s A.D. The Protestant Reformation saw an increase in translations of the Bible into the common languages of the people.

1611 A.D. The King James Bible, translated from Greek, Hebrew, and Aramaic, is completed by 47 scholars for the Church of England, and replaced the Wycliffe Bible as the official English translation of the Bible.

Bible translation continues today! In the last fifty years, Bible scholars and translators have released many new English versions of the Bible, including the New King James Version, the English Standard Version, the New American Standard Bible, the New International Version, the New Living Translation, and many more. The Bible has also been translated into many languages around the world. According to Wycliffe Bible Translators, as of 2015:

- More than 1,300 languages have access to the New Testament and some portions of Scripture in their language.
- More than 550 languages have the complete translated Bible.
- About 7,000 languages are known to be in use today.
- Up to 180 million people need Bible translation to begin in their language.
- Just under 2,300 languages across 130 countries have active translation and linguistic development work happening right now.
- Up to 1,800 languages still need a Bible translation project to begin.

Copying the Scriptures

Most people in our country can read and many own several Bibles. But for a long time, it was very expensive to purchase a Bible. Also, very few people knew how to read. Therefore, few people owned a Bible. Can you imagine not being able to read your favorite book? That would be simply terrible. Some would say we are lucky, but really we are very blessed. If you ever feel like grumbling about your reading time, think about how many books you have. It might help you to have a change in your attitude.

In about 1456, a man named Johannes Gutenburg, invented the printing press. Wonder of wonders, something that used to take years to print by hand, letter by letter, could now be done very quickly on his printing press. That is when books started to become more available and less expensive. We can thank Mr. Gutenburg for making it possible for us to have all the books we want: easy books, hard books, books about math and science, and even books about your favorite games.

You can see very old copies of the Old and New Testaments in museums all around the world. This might be a fun field trip for you and your family to take.

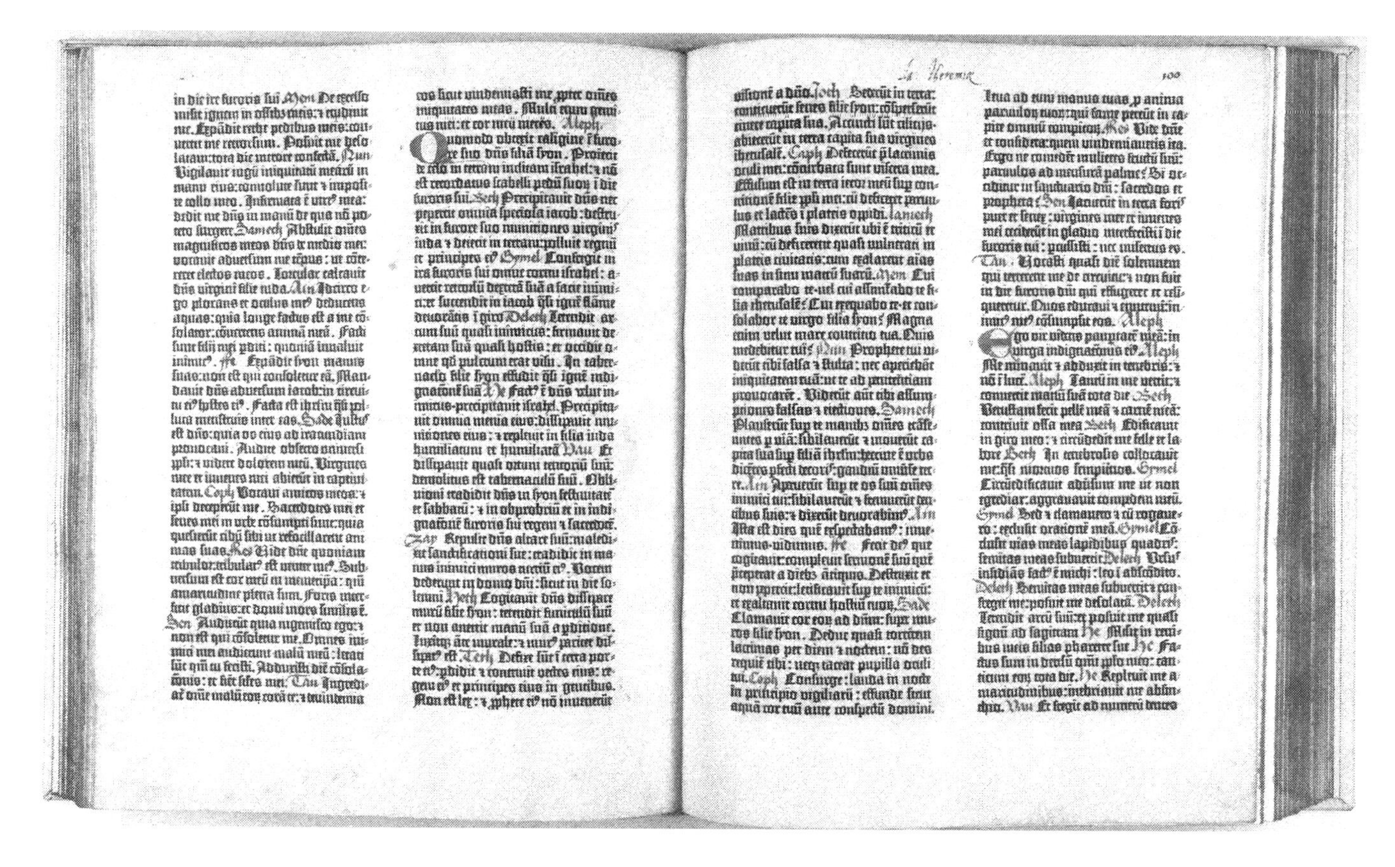

Lesson 21: Day 1

Do not eat the food of a begrudging host, do not crave his delicacies;
for he is the kind of person who is always thinking about the cost.
"Eat and drink," he says to you, but his heart is not with you.
Proverbs 23:6-7 NIV

Trace and copy the verse below.

Do not eat the food

of a begrudging host . . .

Do not eat the food

of a begrudging host . . .

Do not eat the food

of a begrudging host . . .

Lesson 21: Day 2

Do not eat the food of a begrudging host, **do not crave his delicacies;**
for he is the kind of person who is always thinking about the cost.
"Eat and drink," he says to you, but his heart is not with you.
Proverbs 23:6-7 NIV

Trace and copy the verse below.

. . . do not crave

his delicacies;

. . . do not crave

his delicacies;

. . . do not crave

his delicacies;

Lesson 21: Day 3

Do not eat the food of a begrudging host, do not crave his delicacies;
for he is the kind of person who is always thinking about the cost.
"Eat and drink," he says to you, but his heart is not with you.
Proverbs 23:6-7 NIV

Trace and copy the verse below.

. . . for he is the kind of person

who is always thinking about the cost.

. . . for he is the kind of person

who is always thinking about the cost.

Lesson 21: Day 4

Do not eat the food of a begrudging host, do not crave his delicacies;
for he is the kind of person who is always thinking about the cost.
"Eat and drink," he says to you, but his heart is not with you.
Proverbs 23:6-7 NIV

Trace and copy the verse below.

"Eat and drink," he says to you,

but his heart is not with you.

"Eat and drink," he says to you,

but his heart is not with you.

"Eat and drink," he says to you,

but his heart is not with you.

Lesson 22: Day 1

The fool has said in his heart, "There is no God."
They are corrupt, and have done abominable iniquity; There is none who does good.
God looks down from heaven upon the children of men,
To see if there are any who understand, who seek God.
Psalm 53:1-2 NKJV

Trace and copy the verse below.

The fool has said in his heart,

"There is no God."

The fool has said in his heart,

"There is no God."

The fool has said in his heart,

"There is no God."

Lesson 22: Day 2

The fool has said in his heart, "There is no God."
They are corrupt, and have done abominable iniquity; There is none who does good.
God looks down from heaven upon the children of men,
To see if there are any who understand, who seek God.
Psalm 53:1-2 NKJV

Trace and copy the verse below.

They are corrupt, and have done
abominable iniquity;
There is none who does good.

They are corrupt, and have done
abominable iniquity;
There is none who does good.

Lesson 22: Day 3

The fool has said in his heart, "There is no God."
They are corrupt, and have done abominable iniquity; There is none who does good.
God looks down from heaven upon the children of men,
To see if there are any who understand, who seek God.
Psalm 53:1-2 NKJV

Trace and copy the verse below.

God looks down from heaven

upon the children of men . . .

God looks down from heaven

upon the children of men . . .

God looks down from heaven

upon the children of men . . .

Lesson 22: Day 4

The fool has said in his heart, "There is no God."
They are corrupt, and have done abominable iniquity; There is none who does good.
God looks down from heaven upon the children of men,
To see if there are any who understand, who seek God.
Psalm 53:1-2 NKJV

Trace and copy the verse below.

To see if there are any

who understand, who seek God.

To see if there are any

who understand, who seek God.

To see if there are any

who understand, who seek God.

Lesson 23: Day 1

You shall love the LORD your God with all your heart
and with all your soul and with all your might.
And these words that I command you today shall be on your heart.
Deuteronomy 6:5-6 ESV

Trace and copy the verse below.

You shall love the LORD

your God with all your heart . . .

You shall love the LORD

your God with all your heart . . .

You shall love the LORD

your God with all your heart . . .

Lesson 23: Day 2

You shall love the LORD your God with all your heart
and with all your soul and with all your might.
And these words that I command you today shall be on your heart.
Deuteronomy 6:5-6 ESV

Trace and copy the verse below.

. . . and with all your soul

and with all your might.

. . . and with all your soul

and with all your might.

. . . and with all your soul

and with all your might.

Lesson 23: Day 3

You shall love the LORD your God with all your heart
and with all your soul and with all your might.
And these words that I command you today shall be on your heart.
Deuteronomy 6:5-6 ESV

Trace and copy the verse below.

And these words

that I command you . . .

And these words

that I command you . . .

And these words

that I command you . . .

Lesson 23: Day 4

You shall love the LORD your God with all your heart
and with all your soul and with all your might.
And these words that I command you **today shall be on your heart.**
Deuteronomy 6:5-6 ESV

Trace and copy the verse below.

. . . today shall be

on your heart.

. . . today shall be

on your heart.

. . . today shall be

on your heart.

Lesson 24: Day 1

He replied, "Isaiah was right when he prophesied about you hypocrites;
as it is written: " 'These people honor me with their lips,
but their hearts are far from me.' "
Mark 7:6 NIV

Trace and copy the verse below.

He replied, "Isaiah was right

when he prophesied . . ."

He replied, "Isaiah was right

when he prophesied . . ."

He replied, "Isaiah was right

when he prophesied . . ."

Lesson 24: Day 2

He replied, "Isaiah was right when he prophesied **about you hypocrites;**
as it is written: " 'These people honor me with their lips,
but their hearts are far from me.' "
Mark 7:6 NIV

Trace and copy the verse below.

". . . about you hypocrites;

as it is written . . ."

". . . about you hypocrites;

as it is written . . ."

". . . about you hypocrites;

as it is written . . ."

Lessοn 24: Day 3

He replied, "Isaiah was right when he prophesied about you hypocrites;
as it is written: " '**These people honor me with their lips,**
but their hearts are far from me.' "
Mark 7:6 NIV

Trace and copy the verse below.

'These people honor me

with their lips . . .'

'These people honor me

with their lips . . .'

'These people honor me

with their lips . . .'

Lesson 24: Day 4

He replied, "Isaiah was right when he prophesied about you hypocrites;
as it is written: " 'These people honor me with their lips,
but their hearts are far from me.'"
Mark 7:6 NIV

Trace and copy the verse below.

'. . . but their hearts

are far from me."

'. . . but their hearts

are far from me."

'. . . but their hearts

are far from me."

Lesson 25: Day 1

I would have lost heart, unless I had believed
That I would see the goodness of the LORD in the land of the living.
Wait on the LORD; Be of good courage,
And He shall strengthen your heart; Wait, I say, on the LORD!
Psalm 27:13-14 NKJV

Trace and copy the verse below.

I would have lost heart,

unless I had believed . . .

I would have lost heart,

unless I had believed . . .

I would have lost heart,

unless I had believed . . .

Lesson 25: Day 2

I would have lost heart, unless I had believed
That I would see the goodness of the LORD in the land of the living.
Wait on the LORD; Be of good courage,
And He shall strengthen your heart; Wait, I say, on the LORD!
Psalm 27:13-14 NKJV

Trace and copy the verse below.

That I would see the goodness
of the LORD
In the land of the living.

That I would see the goodness
of the LORD
In the land of the living.

Lesson 25: Day 3

I would have lost heart, unless I had believed
That I would see the goodness of the LORD in the land of the living.
Wait on the LORD; Be of good courage,
And He shall strengthen your heart; Wait, I say, on the LORD!
Psalm 27:13-14 NKJV

Trace and copy the verse below.

Wait on the LORD;

Be of good courage . . .

Wait on the LORD;

Be of good courage . . .

Wait on the LORD;

Be of good courage . . .

Lessson 25: Day 4

I would have lost heart, unless I had believed
That I would see the goodness of the LORD in the land of the living.
Wait on the LORD; Be of good courage,
And He shall strengthen your heart; Wait, I say, on the LORD!
Psalm 27:13-14 NKJV

Trace and copy the verse below.

And He shall strengthen your heart;

Wait, I say, on the LORD!

And He shall strengthen your heart;

Wait, I say, on the LORD!

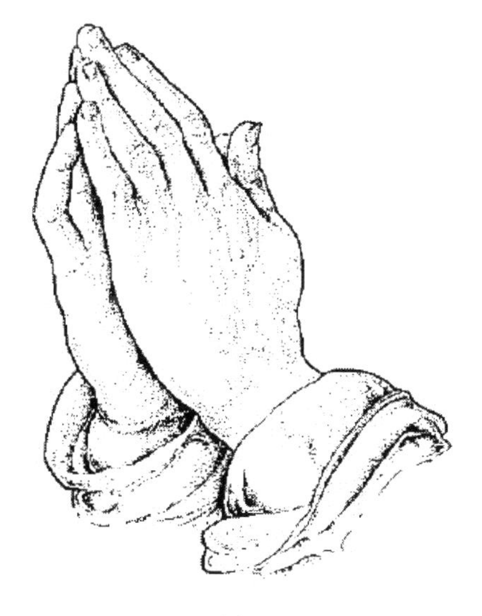

Lesson 26: Day 1

Trust in the LORD with all your heart, and do not rely on your own understanding.
Acknowledge him in all your ways, and he will make your paths straight.
Proverbs 3:5-6 NET

Trace and copy the verse below.

Trust in the LORD

with all your heart . . .

Trust in the LORD

with all your heart . . .

Trust in the LORD

with all your heart . . .

Lesson 26: Day 2

Trust in the LORD with all your heart, **and do not rely on your own understanding.** Acknowledge him in all your ways, and he will make your paths straight.
Proverbs 3:5-6 NET

Trace and copy the verse below.

. . . and do not rely

on your own understanding.

. . . and do not rely

on your own understanding.

. . . and do not rely

on your own understanding.

Lesson 26: Day 3

Trust in the LORD with all your heart, and do not rely on your own understanding.
Acknowledge him in all your ways, and he will make your paths straight.
Proverbs 3:5-6 NET

Trace and copy the verse below.

Acknowledge him

in all your ways . . .

Acknowledge him

in all your ways . . .

Acknowledge him

in all your ways . . .

Lesson 26: Day 4

Trust in the LORD with all your heart, and do not rely on your own understanding. Acknowledge him in all your ways, **and he will make your paths straight.**
Proverbs 3:5-6 NET

Trace and copy the verse below.

. . . and he will make

your paths straight.

. . . and he will make

your paths straight.

. . . and he will make

your paths straight.

Lesson 27: Day 1

Blessed are the pure in heart,
For they shall see God.
Blessed are the peacemakers,
For they shall be called sons of God.
Matthew 5:8-9 NKJV

Trace and copy the verse below.

Blessed are the pure

in heart . . .

Blessed are the pure

in heart . . .

Blessed are the pure

in heart . . .

Lesson 27: Day 2

Blessed are the pure in heart,
For they shall see God.
Blessed are the peacemakers,
For they shall be called sons of God.
Matthew 5:8-9 NKJV

Trace and copy the verse below.

For they shall

see God.

For they shall

see God.

For they shall

see God.

Lesson 27: Day 3

Blessed are the pure in heart,
For they shall see God.
Blessed are the peacemakers,
For they shall be called sons of God.
Matthew 5:8-9 NKJV

Trace and copy the verse below.

Blessed are the

peacemakers . . .

Blessed are the

peacemakers . . .

Blessed are the

peacemakers . . .

Lesson 27: Day 4

Blessed are the pure in heart,
For they shall see God.
Blessed are the peacemakers,
For they shall be called sons of God.
Matthew 5:8-9 NKJV

Trace and copy the verse below.

For they shall be called

sons of God.

For they shall be called

sons of God.

Lesson 28: Day 1

Come and hear, all you who fear God, and I will tell what he has done for my soul.
I cried to him with my mouth, and high praise was on my tongue.
If I had cherished iniquity in my heart, the Lord would not have listened.
But truly God has listened; he has attended to the voice of my prayer.
Psalm 66:16-19 ESV

Trace and copy the verse below.

Come and hear, all you who fear God,

and I will tell what

he has done for my soul.

Come and hear, all you who fear God,

and I will tell what

he has done for my soul.

Lesson 28: Day 2

Come and hear, all you who fear God, and I will tell what he has done for my soul.
I cried to him with my mouth, and high praise was on my tongue.
If I had cherished iniquity in my heart, the Lord would not have listened.
But truly God has listened; he has attended to the voice of my prayer.
Psalm 66:16-19 ESV

Trace and copy the verse below.

I cried to him with my mouth,

and high praise was on my tongue.

I cried to him with my mouth,

and high praise was on my tongue.

I cried to him with my mouth,

and high praise was on my tongue.

Lesson 28: Day 3

Come and hear, all you who fear God, and I will tell what he has done for my soul.
I cried to him with my mouth, and high praise was on my tongue.
If I had cherished iniquity in my heart, the Lord would not have listened.
But truly God has listened; he has attended to the voice of my prayer.
Psalm 66:16-19 ESV

Trace and copy the verse below.

If I had cherished

iniquity in my heart,

the Lord would not have listened.

If I had cherished

iniquity in my heart,

the Lord would not have listened.

Lesson 28: Day 4

Come and hear, all you who fear God, and I will tell what he has done for my soul.
I cried to him with my mouth, and high praise was on my tongue.
If I had cherished iniquity in my heart, the Lord would not have listened.
But truly God has listened; he has attended to the voice of my prayer.
Psalm 66:16-19 ESV

Trace and copy the verse below.

But truly God has listened;

he has attended to the voice

of my prayer.

But truly God has listened;

he has attended to the voice

of my prayer.

Lesson 29: Day 1

And you, Solomon my son, know the God of your father and serve him with a whole heart and with a willing mind, for the LORD searches all hearts and understands every plan and thought. If you seek him, he will be found by you, but if you forsake him, he will cast you off forever.
1 Chronicles 28:9 ESV

Trace and copy the verse below.

"And you, Solomon my son,

know the God of your father . . ."

"And you, Solomon my son,

know the God of your father . . ."

"And you, Solomon my son,

know the God of your father . . ."

Lesson 29: Day 2

And you, Solomon my son, know the God of your father **and serve him with a whole heart and with a willing mind,** for the LORD searches all hearts and understands every plan and thought. If you seek him, he will be found by you, but if you forsake him, he will cast you off forever.
1 Chronicles 28:9 ESV

Trace and copy the verse below.

". . . and serve him with a whole heart

and with a willing mind . . ."

". . . and serve him with a whole heart

and with a willing mind . . ."

". . . and serve him with a whole heart

and with a willing mind . . ."

Lesson 29: Day 3

And you, Solomon my son, know the God of your father and serve him with a whole heart and with a willing mind, **for the LORD searches all hearts and understands every plan and thought.** If you seek him, he will be found by you, but if you forsake him, he will cast you off forever.
1 Chronicles 28:9 ESV

Trace and copy the verse below.

"… for the LORD searches all hearts

and understands every plan

and thought."

"… for the LORD searches all hearts

and understands every plan

and thought."

Lesson 29: Day 4

And you, Solomon my son, know the God of your father and serve him with a whole heart and with a willing mind, for the LORD searches all hearts and understands every plan and thought. **If you seek him, he will be found by you, but if you forsake him, he will cast you off forever.**
1 Chronicles 28:9 ESV

Trace and copy the verse below.

"If you seek him, he will be found
by you, but if you forsake him,
he will cast you off forever."

"If you seek him, he will be found
by you, but if you forsake him,
he will cast you off forever."

Lesson 30: Day 1

Keep back Your servant also from presumptuous sins; Let them not have dominion over me.
Then I shall be blameless, And I shall be innocent of great transgression.
Let the words of my mouth and the meditation of my heart
Be acceptable in Your sight, O LORD, my strength and my Redeemer.
Psalm 19:13-14 NKJV

Trace and copy the verse below.

Keep back Your servant also

from presumptuous sins;

Let them not have dominion over me.

Keep back Your servant also

from presumptuous sins;

Let them not have dominion over me.

Lesson 30: Day 2

Keep back Your servant also from presumptuous sins; Let them not have dominion over me.
Then I shall be blameless, And I shall be innocent of great transgression.
Let the words of my mouth and the meditation of my heart
Be acceptable in Your sight, O LORD, my strength and my Redeemer.
Psalm 19:13-14 NKJV

Trace and copy the verse below.

Then I shall be blameless,

And I shall be innocent

of great transgression.

Then I shall be blameless,

And I shall be innocent

of great transgression.

Lesson 30: Day 3

Keep back Your servant also from presumptuous sins; Let them not have dominion over me.
Then I shall be blameless, And I shall be innocent of great transgression.
Let the words of my mouth and the meditation of my heart
Be acceptable in Your sight, O LORD, my strength and my Redeemer.
Psalm 19:13-14 NKJV

Trace and copy the verse below.

Let the words of my mouth

and the meditation of my heart . . .

Let the words of my mouth

and the meditation of my heart . . .

Let the words of my mouth

and the meditation of my heart . . .

Lesson 30: Day 4

Keep back Your servant also from presumptuous sins; Let them not have dominion over me.
Then I shall be blameless, And I shall be innocent of great transgression.
Let the words of my mouth and the meditation of my heart
Be acceptable in Your sight, O LORD, my strength and my Redeemer.
Psalm 19:13-14 NKJV

Trace and copy the verse below.

Be acceptable in Your sight,

O LORD, my strength

and my Redeemer.

Be acceptable in Your sight,

O LORD, my strength

and my Redeemer.

The Development of the Scriptures

The Bible we read today is made up of 66 books inspired by God, written and collected over many hundreds of years. These writings were originally written in three languages--Hebrew, Aramaic, and Greek--and were copied and translated by scribes, who passed them from generation to generation.

The following timeline shows the development of the books of the Bible in chronological order.

Book	Writer	Date	Language
Genesis	Moses	1513 BC	Hebrew
Exodus	Moses	1512 BC	Hebrew
Leviticus	Moses	1512 BC	Hebrew
Job	Unknown	c. 1473 BC	Hebrew
Numbers	Moses	1473 BC	Hebrew
Deuteronomy	Moses	1473 BC	Hebrew
Joshua	Joshua	c. 1450 BC	Hebrew
Judges	Samuel	c. 1100 BC	Hebrew
Ruth	Samuel	c. 1090 BC	Hebrew
1 Samuel	Samuel, Gad, Nathan	c. 1078 BC	Hebrew
2 Samuel	Gad, Nathan	c. 1040 BC	Hebrew
Song of Solomon	Solomon	c. 1020 BC	Hebrew
Ecclesiastes	Solomon	b. 1000 BC	Hebrew
Jonah	Jonah	c. 844 BC	Hebrew
Joel	Joel	c. 820 BC	Hebrew
Amos	Amos	c. 804 BC	Hebrew
Hosea	Hosea	a. 745 BC	Hebrew
Isaiah	Isaiah	a. 732 BC	Hebrew
Micah	Micah	b. 717 BC	Hebrew
Proverbs	Solomon, Agur, Lemuel	c. 717 BC	Hebrew
Zephaniah	Zephaniah	b. 648 BC	Hebrew
Nahum	Nahum	b. 632 BC	Hebrew
Habakkuk	Habakkuk	c. 628 BC	Hebrew
Lamentations	Jeremiah	607 BC	Hebrew
Obadiah	Obadiah	c. 607 BC	Hebrew
Ezekiel	Ezekiel	c. 591 BC	Hebrew
1 and 2 Kings	Jeremiah	580 BC	Hebrew
Jeremiah	Jeremiah	580 BC	Hebrew
Daniel	Daniel	c. 536 BC	Hebrew, Aramaic
Haggai	Haggai	520 BC	Hebrew
Zechariah	Zechariah	518 BC	Hebrew
Esther	Mordecai	c. 475 BC	Hebrew

The Development of the Scriptures

B.C.: Before Christ
A.D.: *anno Domini* ("in the year of the Lord")

c.: circa (around)
a.: after
b.: before

Book	Writer	Date	Language
1 and 2 Chronicles	Ezra	c. 460 BC	Hebrew
Ezra	Ezra	c. 460 BC	Hebrew, Aramaic
Psalms	David and others	c. 1000 to 460 BC	Hebrew
Nehemiah	Nehemiah	a. 443 BC	Hebrew
Malachi	Malachi	a. 443 BC	Hebrew
Matthew	Matthew	c. AD 41	Greek
1 Thessalonians	Paul	c. AD 51	Greek
2 Thessalonians	Paul	c. AD 52	Greek
Galatians	Paul	c. AD 50-52	Greek
1 Corinthians	Paul	c. AD 57	Greek
2 Corinthians	Paul	c. AD 58	Greek
Romans	Paul	c. AD 58	Greek
Luke	Luke	c. AD 56-58	Greek
Ephesians	Paul	c. AD 60-61	Greek
Colossians	Paul	c. AD 60-61	Greek
Philemon	Paul	c. AD 60-61	Greek
Philippians	Paul	c. AD 60-61	Greek
Hebrews	believed to be Paul	c. AD 61	Greek
Acts	Luke	c. AD 61	Greek
James	James (Jesus' brother)	b. AD 62	Greek
Mark	Mark	c. AD 60-65	Greek
1 Timothy	Paul	c. AD 61-65	Greek
Titus	Paul	c. AD 61-65	Greek
1 Peter	Peter	c. AD 62-64	Greek
2 Peter	Peter	c. AD 64	Greek
2 Timothy	Paul	c. AD 67	Greek
Jude	Jude (Jesus' brother)	c. AD 65	Greek
Revelation	Apostle John	c. AD 96	Greek
John	Apostle John	c. AD 98	Greek
1 John	Apostle John	c. AD 98	Greek
2 John	Apostle John	c. AD 98	Greek
3 John	Apostle John	c. AD 98	Greek

Items available from Laurelwood Books

Ōlim, Once Upon a Time, in Latin Series

Readers and Workbooks
(Supplementary audio files available for all Latin titles)

Book I: *The Three Little Pigs, The Tortoise and the Hare, The Crow and the Pitcher*
Book II: *The Ant and the Chrysalis, The Lost Sheep, The Good Samaritan*
Book III: *The Feeding of the 5,000, The Lion and the Mouse*
Book IV: *Creation*
Book V: *Daniel, Part I; We Know a Tree by its Fruit*
Book VI: *The Prodigal Son*
Book VII: *David and Goliath*
Book VIII: *Daniel, Part II*
Book IX: *Daniel, Part III, The Miser*
Book X: *The Wise Man and Foolish Man, The Ten Maidens*

Ōlim Derivatives I, II
Latin Verbs: To Infinitives and Beyond! Book I, II, III
Latin for Littles, Vol I

Scripture Scribes Series

Pre-Primary: *From Scribbler to Scribe*

Primary: *Who Made Me?, My Whole Heart, His Name Is Wonderful, Psalms & Proverbs for Young Catholics, Practicing Proverbs, Following Jesus with Scripture, Song, and Art*

Intermediate: *One Another, Savoring Psalms, Foundations of Faith*

Upper School: *Men of Honor & Women of Grace, Walking With God*

Extra Practice Workbooks: Primary, Intermediate
(For use with Patriotic Penmanship and Scripture Scribes)

Made in the USA
San Bernardino, CA
05 August 2020

76560187R00075